# Detective Dog™
## and The Lost Rabbit

D1054958

# Detective Dog™
## and The Lost Rabbit

Written by Leslie McGuire
Illustrated by Mitchell Rose

HOOKED ON
PHONICS™

# Contents

## Special Words

Special words help make this story fun.
Your child may need help reading them.

cow

detective

footprint

house

# 1 A Big Job

I am Detective Dog. I look
for lost pets. I get the pets back.

BAM! BAM! BAM!
It is Fox.
I say, "What do you want?"

"I need you to look for Rabbit,"
says Fox. "He is my pet."
"Why did he run off?" I say.
"He did not say," says Fox.

"That's odd," I say, "but I can get Rabbit back for you."

"Good," says Fox.

"Where did you see him?" I say.

"In my den," says Fox.

I go to Fox's den. No Rabbit. But I see Rabbit's fuzz. I look up the hill. I see fuzz up the hill too.

I bet that's Rabbit's fuzz, and
I bet he's up the hill. I will get
him back now.

It's a BIG hill. I huff
and puff up the hill. But
what I see is NOT Rabbit.
What I see upsets me.

# What Is Rabbit Up To?!?!

It is Pig. Pig looks mad.
"I had lots of eggs," says Pig.
"Now I do not!"
  "That's too bad," I say.

"I bet Rabbit got the eggs!"
says Pig. "I want you to get
my eggs back!"

"I am on a big job," I say.
"I cannot get your eggs
back now."

"That's too bad," says Pig.
"Did you see Rabbit?" I say.
"Yes. He went that way," says Pig.

"Thank you," I say.
"Can we come too?" says Pig.
"Yes," I say.

Pig, the hens, and I go look for Rabbit.

"Look!" I say. "Is that Rabbit's fuzz in the mud?"

We see footprints in the mud too. Are the footprints Rabbit's footprints?

No. The footprints are
Cat's footprints.
"What do you want?" says Cat.

"We need to get Rabbit," I say.
"I do too," says Cat. "I had
a bag of nuts, but I think Rabbit
has the bag now."

"Did you see him?" I say.
"Yes," says Cat. "He went
that way."

"I will go look," I say.
"Can I come, too?" says Cat.
"Yes," I say.

Pig, the hens, and Cat come
with me. We see a pit with fuzz
in it. We see Bug in the fuzz.
"Did you see Rabbit?" I say.

"Yes," says Bug. "He went that way. But he got my jam, and I want it back."

"Come with us," says Pig.

Pig, the hens, Cat, Bug, and
I go look for Rabbit.
We get to the mill.
What is that?
Now THAT looks BAD!

# 3 Rabbit Is BAD!

Duck and Cow are at the mill.
Duck is upset! Cow looks bad!
  "Did you see Rabbit?" I say.
  "You bet I did!" says Cow.

"He got into the mill!"
yells Duck.

"He got my milk!" sobs
Cow. "Lots of it!"

"This is not good," I say.
"I need to think."

I go sit on a rock. I get
out my pad.

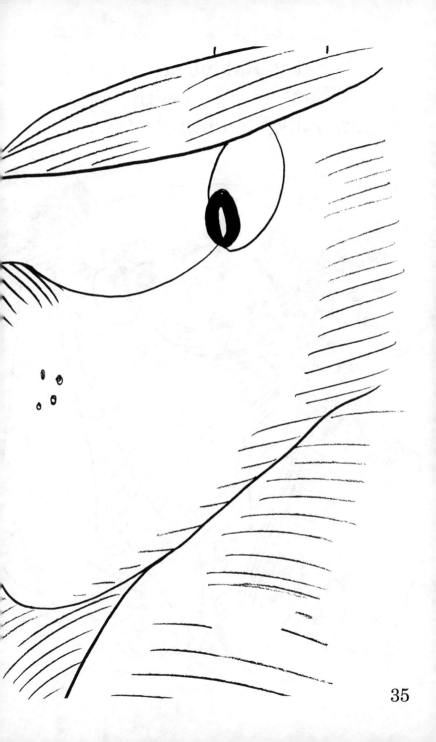

What is Rabbit up to?
What can he do with eggs,
jam, milk, and nuts?

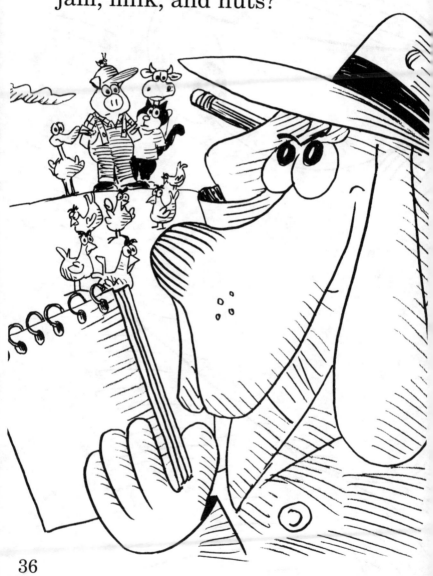

"Let's go back and see what
Fox thinks," I say.

"We will go with you,"
say Pig, the hens, Cat, Bug,
Duck, and Cow.

We get to Fox's den, but
Fox is not in his den!
"Now where is Fox?" I say.
I get out my pad.

As I get up, Fox runs up
to us.

"I think I can get him!"
yells Fox.

"Where?" I say.

"That way!" yells Fox.

"Let's go get him now!" yell
Cow, the hens, Pig, Duck, Cat,
and Bug.

We run up the hill. I do NOT
like what I see!

"This is MY house!" I say.

"Yes," says Fox. "You go in and look."

"Me?" I say. "I need to look in MY house for Rabbit? This is too odd!"

Rabbit is in MY house!
"SURPRISE!"

"HAPPY BIRTHDAY!" yell
Fox, Rabbit, Pig, the hens, Cat,
Bug, Cow, and Duck.
"Why, thank you," I say.

"Did you make this cake with the eggs, jam, nuts, and milk?" I say.

"Yes," says Rabbit.

"Why did you make me go look for you?" I say.

"I had to get you out of the house to make the cake."

See? It can be fun to be a
detective! This is good cake, too!